Growing Mr Greenhead

Pam Mayo

Contents

OXFORD
UNIVERSITY PRESS

OXFORD
UNIVERSITY PRESS

Great Clarendon Street, Oxford, OX2 6DP

Oxford University Press is a department of the University of Oxford.
It furthers the University's objective of excellence in research, scholarship,
and education by publishing worldwide in

Oxford New York

Athens Auckland Bangkok Bogotá Buenos Aires Calcutta
Cape Town Chennai Dar es Salaam Delhi Florence Hong Kong Istanbul
Karachi Kuala Lumpur Madrid Melbourne Mexico City Mumbai
Nairobi Paris São Paulo Singapore Taipei Tokyo Toronto Warsaw
and associated companies in Berlin Ibadan

Oxford is a registered trade mark of Oxford University Press
in the UK and in certain other countries

First published by Oxford University Press 1999
Reprinted 1999

A CIP record for this book is available from the British Library

ISBN 0 19 915768 5
Available in packs
Pack B Pack of Six   (one of each book)   ISBN 0 19 915771 5
Pack B Class Pack   (six of each book)   ISBN 0 19 915772 3

Printed in Hong Kong

Acknowledgements

Photography on p 3 by Mark Mason.
All other photography by Martin Sookias

With thanks to Ruth Hodgson and George Readshaw.

Front cover photograph by Martin Sookias
Back cover photographs by Mark Mason

Introduction

This book will tell you how to make a Mr Greenhead. This is what you need.

compost

elastic band

a sock

water

yoghurt pot

grass seed

glue

felt

scissors

Grass seed and compost

First, put grass seed in the sock.

grass
seed

sock

Next, put in
the compost.

compost

Making Mr Greenhead stand up

Put an elastic band around the sock. Cut the end off the sock.

elastic band

Put the sock in the yoghurt pot.
The elastic
band should
be at the
bottom.

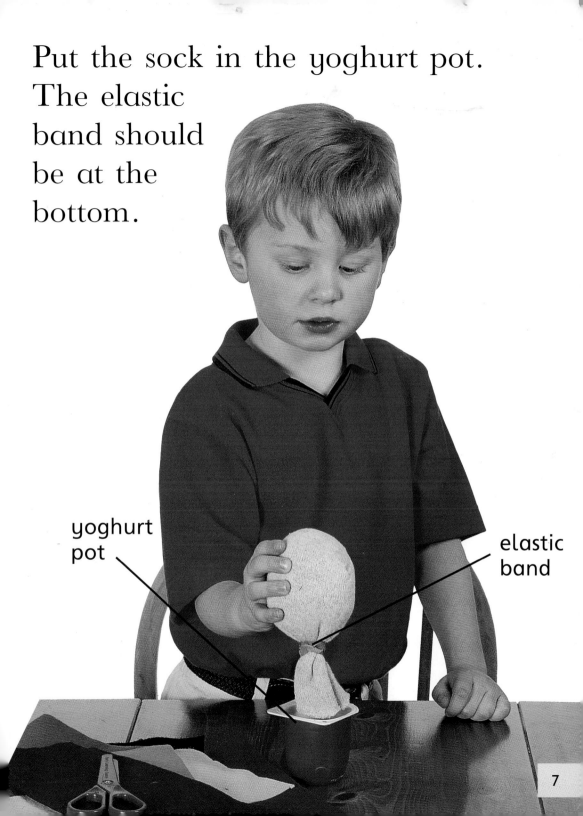

yoghurt
pot

elastic
band

Mr Greenhead's face

Next, cut a face out of felt.

scissors

felt

Stick the face on with glue.

glue

Watching Mr Greenhead grow

Water the top of the sock every day.

Day 3

Day 10

Day 14

Warning!
Do not make
Mr Greenhead
too soggy!

11

Index

Pepper's Travels with Marco Polo

by **Nancy Harris**

illustrated by Filippo Vanzo

a Capstone company — publishers for children

Engage Literacy is published in the UK by Raintree.
Raintree is an imprint of Capstone Global Library Limited, a company
incorporated in England and Wales having its registered office at
264 Banbury Road, Oxford, OX2 7DY – Registered company number:
6695582

www.raintree.co.uk

10 9 8 7 6 5 4 3 2

Printed and bound in India.

Pepper's Travels with Marco Polo

ISBN: 978-1-4747-1789-2

Contents

Chapter 1
Meeting Marco

I woke before sunrise, staring into the darkness of our tent. I was too excited to sleep. My father and I were on a trip along the Silk Road. My father was a trader of spices, such as cinnamon and nutmeg. We had just arrived in China on our trip to get riches from all around the world.

Later in the morning, my father said, "Pepper, go into the city to get food for breakfast." He was going into town to get more supplies. My father calls me Pepper because I sneeze whenever I get near spices.

"I will meet you later. Wait for me by the river with the large waterfall. Don't jump in," he said with a wink.

Later that day, I was sitting near the river waiting for my father. A teenage boy sat next to me. "Hello, my name is Marco Polo," he said. "My father, uncle and I have come from Italy to see Kublai Khan, the great leader of China."

I had never seen anyone wearing clothes like his. "He must be important," I thought. "He knows a great leader."

"My father and I are from an island thousands of miles away," I told Marco. "We heard that you could make a fortune here, trading for colourful cloth, unusual spices and gems."

"Yes, there is a beautiful soft cloth called silk," Marco said. "It is made by worms, and people will pay a high price for one colourful piece."

We talked until our fathers met us by the river. "We are heading east tomorrow to meet a caravan of traders. You should travel with us," suggested Marco's father.

"Thank you," said my father. "We will cross the large desert with you."

Chapter 2

Danger in the darkness

We left early the next morning. First, we travelled through a thick forest. There were growling noises all around us. "Look out!" I shouted. Two huge creatures, each with a large horn, were running straight at us!

Marco Polo turned and shouted at us to get out of the way. "GO! GO! GO!" he cried. Unfortunately the creatures had already run past us and squashed three bags of food. "At least we were able to save the rest of our supplies." Marco said, looking at the mess.

The next day Marco's father said, "We'll have to travel all day and all night to meet the caravan." But that evening, it was too dark to travel. We were going to have to wait.

Then suddenly, something magical happened. "Look! There are hundreds of shiny balls of light floating in the sky!" I shouted.

"They are floating lanterns," Marco explained. "We can use them to light our way.

Chapter 3
Travelling across the desert

The following morning we met up with the caravan. There were traders from China, Persia and Greece. They had brought ginger, colourful silk and other goods to trade. They were packing their supplies onto the backs of strange animals that I had never seen before. The animals had round ears, skinny legs and two large humps on their backs.

"What is that?" I asked.

"It's a camel," Marco replied. Then he showed me how to load supplies onto the camel's back.

The caravan left before sunrise. It was still a bit cool outside. But by midday the desert was hot and dry.

We travelled across the hot desert all day. Then we set up camp and went to sleep. A strange voice woke me in the middle of the night.

"Quick, loosen the ropes!" said the stranger.

I ran outside and discovered three robbers trying to steal our camels. "Help! Robbers! Help!" I screamed as I chased them.

Marco came out, shouting, "Where? Where?" But the robbers had already escaped into a cloud of desert dust.

Luckily, they had left the loose camels behind. "Let's split up and gather the camels before they wander too far away," Marco said.

After walking for a while, I heard the bells around the camels' necks ringing. I gathered up a few camels and headed back to the caravan. But all I could see was sand blowing all around.

Marco must have also heard the bells because he found me in the sandstorm. We travelled back through the swirling sand to our camp. "For such a young boy, you are truly a brave and wise traveller," Marco told me.

I had never felt prouder.

Chapter 4

More animal adventures

After crossing the desert, my father and I left the caravan along with the Polos and kept heading east. Many days later, we finally arrived at one of Kublai Khan's palaces.

"Look at all the gold," I whispered.

The next day, Marco's father and uncle met with Kublai Khan. My father was out trading.

"There must be a million trees in that forest over there. Let's go for a hike!" I suggested to Marco. He agreed.

Suddenly we felt the earth shaking under our feet. "We're going to be swallowed up by the ground!" Marco said with fear in his voice.

But the ground was shaking because a huge elephant was running towards us. The elephant was pulling a cart with a large tree in it. "It's running this way! Watch out!" I shouted.

Right in front of us, the elephant stopped. It bent down to move a log that was in its way. My father and I had worked with elephants back home. I knew I had to act quickly. I climbed on the elephant's back and steered it away from Marco. "Watch out! Move back!" I shouted. Marco stepped backwards into a cold pond. He came out shivering and shaking his head.

That night at dinner, Marco told the elephant story. Everyone laughed. "It's a wonder you thought to ride on the elephant," Marco's uncle said. "And I'm sure that Marco needed that ice-cold bath!"

17

The next morning Marco and I decided to go fishing in one of the ponds near the palace. We hiked up a rocky hill and almost fell into a large blue pond. "What is that splashing sound?" I asked. There were many different types of fish jumping in and out of the water.

"Whoever catches the fewest fish has to cook dinner tonight," Marco said. I sat down on a rock and started fishing. The fish seemed to be flying onto my hook, one right after the other.

After an hour, I had caught twice as many fish as Marco. "You are the better fisherman," Marco said. "I'll carry the heavy fish baskets back to the palace."

Marco cooked dinner that night. Then we all had a good laugh about our fishing adventure. Well, everyone except Marco had a good laugh.

Chapter 5
Growing up with Marco

Over the next few years, we continued to travel around Khan's empire. I was now a young man, and Marco was an older and wiser man.

The empire that Khan ruled over was very large. Khan used messengers to quickly get information from one place to another.

One day when we were out riding, we saw a messenger whose horse was hurt. "I'll let the messenger ride my horse, and you and I can ride your horse," Marco said.

When Marco jumped off his horse, the messenger quickly jumped on and sped off. Marco was knocked to the ground. "That was kind of you," I said, laughing.

"Stop laughing! He could have run me over!" Marco said with a half smile. "Next time, I'll let him take your horse!"

Kublai Khan often sent Marco on trips to faraway places in his empire. Sometimes I would travel with him to trade in the city markets.

"Go to the huge market in the middle of the square," Marco said. "It's full of colourful silk and spices from all over the world. You should have good luck trading there."

I traded all day until it was time to meet Marco for dinner.

"Look at the piles of colourful silk cloth and baskets of spices that I got today. My father will be pleased with the trading I have done," I said proudly. I had started the day with little to trade and ended up with baskets full of goods.

Chapter 6
Going home

After many more years of trading and travelling, my father and I were ready to go home. Marco, his father and his uncle decided to travel with us. "Let's pack up and start the long journey home," my father said.

On the way home, we stopped in a port city and traded by the sea for a few days. "This was a very successful few days of trading. We are now more than ready to go home," said my father. He was dragging baskets of spices, gems and cotton cloth.

The next day we boarded a large ship that would take us home. We noticed that there were several small boats tied to the side of our large ship. "What are those smaller boats used for, and why are there so many?" my father asked, as we walked on the deck.

"They are probably used for fishing in shallow waters," Marco's father replied.

"I heard that traders jump in them, lower them down and row away when they see pirate ships on the horizon," teased Marco's uncle.

Marco's uncle might have been joking, but I knew that pirates were no laughing matter.

That evening, Marco and I sat on the ship's upper deck. I noticed another ship off in the distance. "Look! A pirate ship!" I exclaimed.

"Go get our fathers and my uncle!" Marco instructed. "Gather what you can and meet me here."

"How are we going to hide from the pirates with all these goods?" whispered Marco's father. "The pirates are already climbing over the ship's railing!"

Marco waved us over, and we carefully jumped down into one of the small hanging boats. The pirates scrambled right past us.

After they sailed away, we climbed out of the hanging boat. We had fooled them!

The ocean journey to our island was a long and bumpy trip. Many passengers became very ill from the choppy waves.

When we were safely home my father said, "We are lucky to have made it to shore." Everyone agreed. We were all overjoyed to be safe and sound.

That evening the winds were really howling. "It won't be safe for you to travel home until the winds die down," I told Marco. "That could take months because it's our rainy season."

It was a difficult time for the Polos. They had to stay on our island for months, not knowing when they could sail for home. When the winds finally calmed down, they boarded a ship and headed home.

Marco went on to become a famous explorer. He even wrote a book about his adventures, including some he had with me!

I never saw Marco and his family again. But I never forgot our friendship and the amazing adventures we had along the Silk Road.